Einojuhani Rauta...

A CHILDREN'S MASS

for SA voices and string orchestra

VOCAL SCORE

63

Chorus

SARJA
SERIES

Dedicated to Erkki Pohjola

Einojuhani Rautavaara
LAPSIMESSU
A CHILDREN'S MASS

I Kyrie
II Meditatio super Kyrie
III Gloria
IV Meditatio super Gloriam
V Agnus Dei
VI Meditatio super Agnum Dei
VII Halleluja

Osat Kyrie, Gloria, Agnus Dei ja Halleluja voidaan esittää myös erillisenä messuna a cappella.
Samoin Meditaatiot voidaan esittää erillisenä orkesterisarjana.

Teos voitti ensimmäisen palkinnon Espoon kaupungin sävellyskilpailussa 1973.

The vocal movements Kyrie, Gloria, Agnus Dei and Halleluja may be performed separately (a cappella)
without strings. Similarly the Meditations may be performed separately, as a suite for strings.

This work won first prize in the competition for composers held by
the municipality of Espoo in 1973.

ISMN 979-0-55009-233-4

Printed by Painojussit Oy, Kerava 2008

Lapsimessu
A Children's Mass

I Kyrie

EINOJUHANI RAUTAVAARA 1973

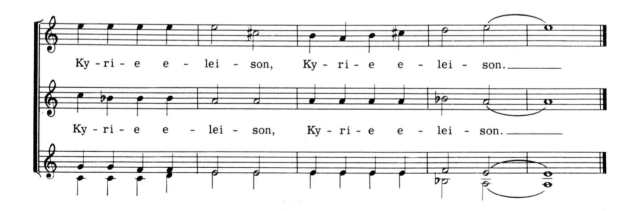

II Meditatio super Kyrie

Tacet

III Gloria

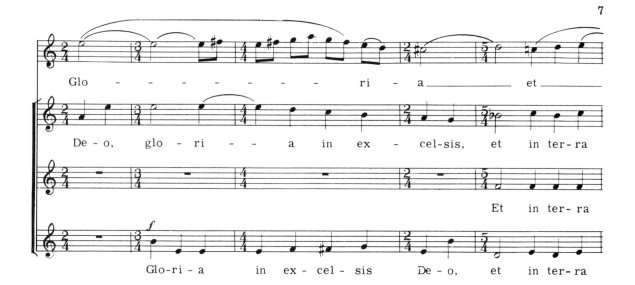

IV Meditatio super Gloriam

Tacet

V Agnus Dei

Ag-nus De — i, mi-se-re-re, mi-se — re — re no — bis.

pec — ca-ta mun-di, mi — se — re — re no — bis.

Ag — — nus, mi-se-re — re no — bis, no — bis.

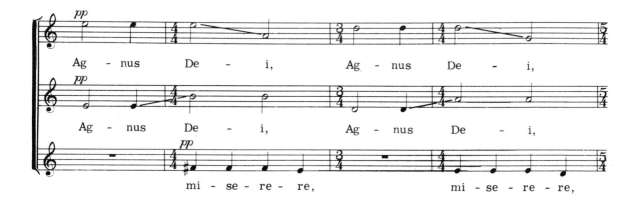

Ag — nus De — i, Ag — nus De — i,

Ag — nus De — i, Ag — nus De — i,

mi — se — re — re, mi — se — re — re,

do — na no — bis pa — — cem.

do — na no — bis pa — — cem.

do — na no — bis pa — — cem.

VI Meditatio super Agnum Dei

Tacet

VII Halleluja

Chorus SERIES

Unless otherwise mentioned, all works are for mixed choir a cappella.

DISTRIBUTED BY HAL LEONARD

0 73999 16295 0
48016295

FENNICA GEHRMAN

KL 78.34

ISMN 979-0-55009-233-4

9 790550 092334